Little Duck Dance

Donna Alvermann
Connie A. Bridge
Barbara A. Schmidt
Lyndon W. Searfoss
Peter Winograd
Scott G. Paris

D.C. Heath and Company
HEATH Lexington, Massachusetts   Toronto, Ontario

Acknowledgments

Grateful acknowledgment is made for permission to reprint the following copyrighted material.

Asch, Frank. **Just Like Daddy** is reprinted by permission of Prentice-Hall, Inc., Englewood Cliffs, N.J. Copyright © 1981 by the Author.

Barchas, Sarah E. **"I Was Walking Down the Road,"** copyright © 1975 by Sarah E. Barchas, is adapted by permission of Scholastic, Inc.

Chute, Marchette. **"Art"** is reprinted from *Rhymes About the City*, copyright 1946, by Marchette Chute. Used by permission of the author.

Chute, Marchette. **"My Family"** and **"My Kitten,"** from *Rhymes About Us*, E.P. Dutton & Co., copyright © 1974 by Marchette Chute, are reprinted by permission of the Author.

Emberley, Edward R. **"Drawing Animals,"** from *Ed Emberley's Drawing Book of Animals*, copyright © 1970 by Edward R. Emberley. By permission of Little, Brown & Company.

Fisher, Aileen. **"New Neighbors"** is reprinted from *In One Door and Out the Other: A Book of Poems*, by Aileen Fisher; copyright © 1969 by Aileen Fisher, by permission of Thomas Y. Crowell Company.

Guterman, Arthur. **"Chums"** is reprinted by permission of Louise H. Sclove.

Isadora, Rachel. **Willaby** is reprinted by permission of Macmillan Publishing Company from *Willaby*, by Rachel Isadora. Copyright © 1977 by Rachel Isadora.

Lenski, Lois. **"A Man"** and **"Up and Down the Street"** from *The Life I Live*, by Lois Lenski, copyright © 1965, are reprinted by permission of the Lois Lenski Covey Foundation, Inc.

Livingston, Myra Cohn. **"Whispers,"** from *Whispers and Other Poems*, by Myra Cohn Livingston, copyright © 1958 by Myra Cohn Livingston, is reprinted by permission of Marian Reiner for the Author.

Milne, A. A. **"The End"** from *Now We Are Six* by A. A. Milne, copyright by E.P. Dutton, renewed 1955 by A. A. Milne. Reprinted by permission of E.P. Dutton & Company.

Moore, Lilian. **"Something Is There,"** from *Spooky Rhymes and Riddles*, by Lilian Moore, copyright © 1975 by Lilian Moore, is reprinted by permission of Scholastic, Inc.

Nŏdset, Joan L. **Go Away Dog**, copyright © 1963 by Joan L. Nŏdset, is adapted by permission of Harper & Row, Publishers, Inc.

Reeves, James. **"Run a Little"** from *The Wandering Moon and Other Poems* (Puffin Books) by James Reeves. Reprinted by permission of the James Reeves Estate.

Soule, Jean Conder. **"Surprises,"** copyright © by Jean Conder Soule. Reprinted by permission.

Thaler, Mike. **Owly**, copyright © 1982 by Michael C. Thaler, is reprinted by permission of Harper & Row, Publishers, Inc.

Van Leeuwen, Jean. **"The Secret"** is adapted from *Amanda Pig and Her Big Brother Oliver*, by Jean Van Leeuwen. Text copyright © 1982 by Jean Van Leeuwen. Reprinted by permission of the publisher, Dial Books for Young Readers.

Cover/Cluster Openers **Design:** Studio Goodwin-Sturges. **Illustration:** Diane Stanley. **Calligraphy:** Colleen.

Editorial **Book Editor:** Laura A. Tills. **Senior Editor:** Susan D. Paro. **Editorial Services:** Marianna Frew Palmer, K. Kirschbaum Harvie. **Permissions Editor:** Dorothy Burns McLeod.
Design **Series:** Leslie Dews. **Book:** Kathy Reynolds, Ingrid Cooper.
Production Mary Hunter.

Illustration **8–13:** Hilary Knight. **18–31:** Frank Asch, copyright © 1981, from *Just Like Daddy*, with permission. **34–37:** Gary Fujiwara. **38–43:** Wendy Edelson. **45–51:** Anthony Accardo. **54–61:** Dennis Hockerman. **62–63:** Mary Jane Begin. **72–80:** Alan K. Daniel. **88–89, 118–125:** Lydia Dabcovich. **110:** Shelly Haas. **111–117:** Ann Schweninger, copyright © 1982, from *Amanda Pig and Her Big Brother Oliver* with permission. **128–138:** Stella Ormai. **140–149:** Mary Szilagyi. **152–153:** Jennifer Levey. **154–157:** Ed Emberley, copyright © 1970, from *Ed Emberley's Drawing Book of Animals*, with permission. **158–167:** Rachel Isadora, copyright © 1977, from *Willaby*, with permission. **178–192:** David Wiesner, copyright © 1982, from *Owly*, with permission.

Photography **14–17:** Ken O'Donoghue © D.C. Heath. **36–37:** Jeffrey Coolidge © D.C. Heath. **44:** Ken O'Donoghue © D.C. Heath. **64–69:** Jeffrey Dunn © D.C. Heath. **81:** C.C. Lockwood (DRK Photo). **82:** Marty Cordano (DRK Photo). **83:** *t,* Bruce Iverson; *b,* Grant Heilman. **84:** *t,* Bruce Iverson; *b,* Grant Heilman. **85:** *t,* Norman Owen Tomalin (Bruce Coleman Inc); *b,* Eric Crichton (Bruce Coleman Inc). **86:** *t,* Norman Owen Tomalin (Bruce Coleman Inc); *b,* Patti Murray (Animals Animals). **87:** *tl, tr,* Jeff Foott (DRK Photo); *cl,* Martin Rotker, (Taurus); *cr,* Alan Pitcairn (Grant Heilman); *bl,* Barry Runk (Grant Heilman); *br,* John R. Hicks (DRK Photo). **102–109:** Ken O'Donoghue © D.C. Heath. **139:** Ralph Mercer © D.C. Heath. **152–153:** Ken O'Donoghue © D.C. Heath. **170:** *t,* Jeff Foott; *c,* Tom Bledsoe (Photo Researchers); *b,* Stephen J. Kraseman (DRK Photo). **171:** Phil Degginger (CLICK/Chicago). **172–173:** Stephen J. Kraseman (DRK Photo). **174, 175:** Jeff Foott. **176:** *t,* L. Lee Rue III (Animals Animals); *cl,* Stephen J. Kraseman (DRK Photo); *br,* Jeff Foott.
Photo Coordinator: Connie Komack. **Photo Research:** Nina Whitney. **Photo Styling:** Elizabeth Willis, June Martin, Nanci Lindholm.

Published simultaneously in Canada

Printed in the United States of America

International Standard Book Number: 0-669-23527-X

3   4   5   6   7   8   9   0

Table of Contents

Who's Next Door?

Surprise! Surprise!

2

Whispers and Smiles

Who's Afraid?

Picture This!

Growing Up

Part of my family is grown-up and tall.
Part of my family is little and small.
I'm in the middle and pleased with them all.

MY FAMILY *by Marchette Chute*

Families

Lee and His Grandma

by Stephanie Calmenson

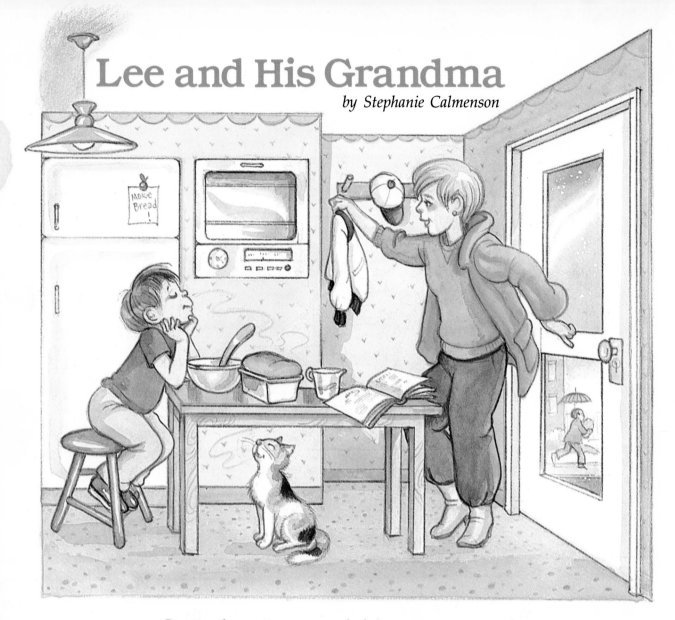

One day Lee and his mom made some bread.

"This is good bread," said Lee. "Can we share it with Grandma?"

"We can go to her house now," said Mom.

That very morning Grandma
made a paper flower.

"This is a fine flower," she said
to her dog Max. "I will share it
with Lee!"

On the way to see Grandma, Lee and his mom passed a flower shop. They got a flower for Grandma.

On her way to see Lee, Grandma passed a bake shop. She got Lee some bread.

Lee and his mom
went all the way
to see Grandma
at her house.
But no one was home!

Grandma and Max went all the
way to see Lee at his house. But no
one was home!

Lee was sad.
He went home
with his head down.

Grandma was sad.
She went home with
her head down too.

It was good that Lee looked up when he did.

"Look!" said Lee. "It is Grandma!"

"Hello, Lee," said Grandma. "I have some bread and a flower for you."

"This is funny," said Lee. "I have some bread and a flower for you too!"

They all went to Grandma's house to eat some bread.

My Family

by Kim Chen

This is my family. I live with
my mom and my dad. I live with
my big sister and my little brother too.

My brother is very little. I have
to help him get dressed. I help him
put on his coat, mittens, and boots.

My sister and I
help Mom and Dad.
One day we helped
them make lunch.
We had pizza.
We like pizza!

This is my uncle.
He is my mom's brother.
He is family too. I like to stay
at his house. We cook lots
of good things. We have fun!

This is my grandma.
She is my dad's mom!
She is family too. I like
to stay at her house.
We like to paint.
We have fun too!

Now you know **my** family.
Who is in **your** family?

Just Like Daddy

by Frank Asch

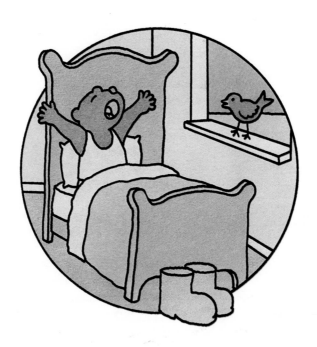

When I got up this morning
I yawned a big yawn . . .

Just like Daddy.

I washed my face,
got dressed, and had
a big breakfast . . .

Just like Daddy.

Then I put on
my coat and
my boots . . .

Just like Daddy.

And we all went fishing.

On the way
I picked a flower
and gave it to
my mother . . .

Just like Daddy.

When we got to the lake, I put a big worm on my hook . . .

Just like Daddy.

All day we fished
and fished, and I
caught a big fish . . .

Just like Mommy!

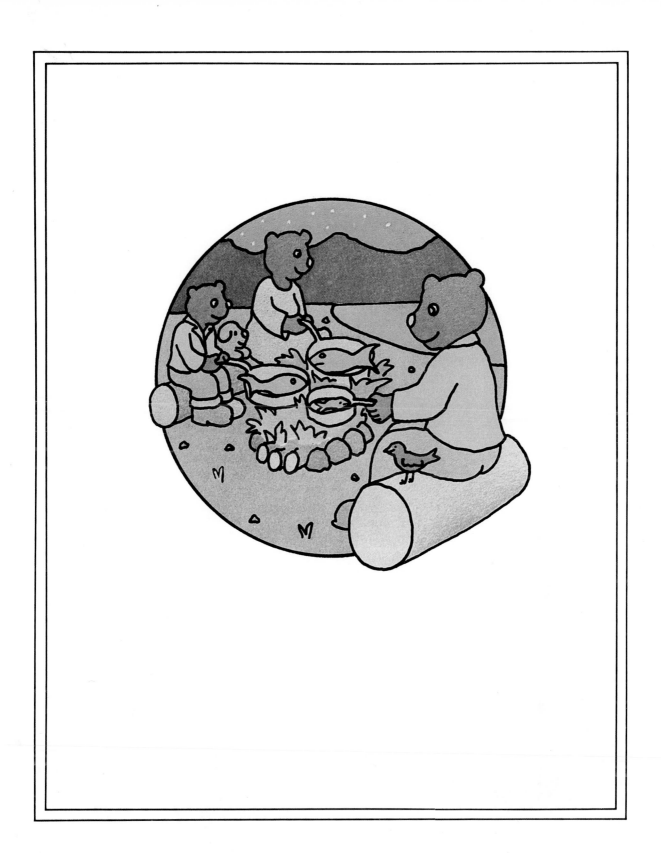

Animal Pals

He sits and begs; he gives a paw;
    He is, as you can see,
The finest dog you ever saw,
    And he belongs to me.

He follows everywhere I go
    And even when I swim.
I laugh because he thinks, you know,
    That I belong to him.

CHUMS *by Arthur Guiterman*

Pet Puppets

by Laura Tills

Here is how you can
make a pet puppet.

You need:

thin white paper

scissors

tape

pencils and crayons

1. Trace a pet
   on thin white paper.

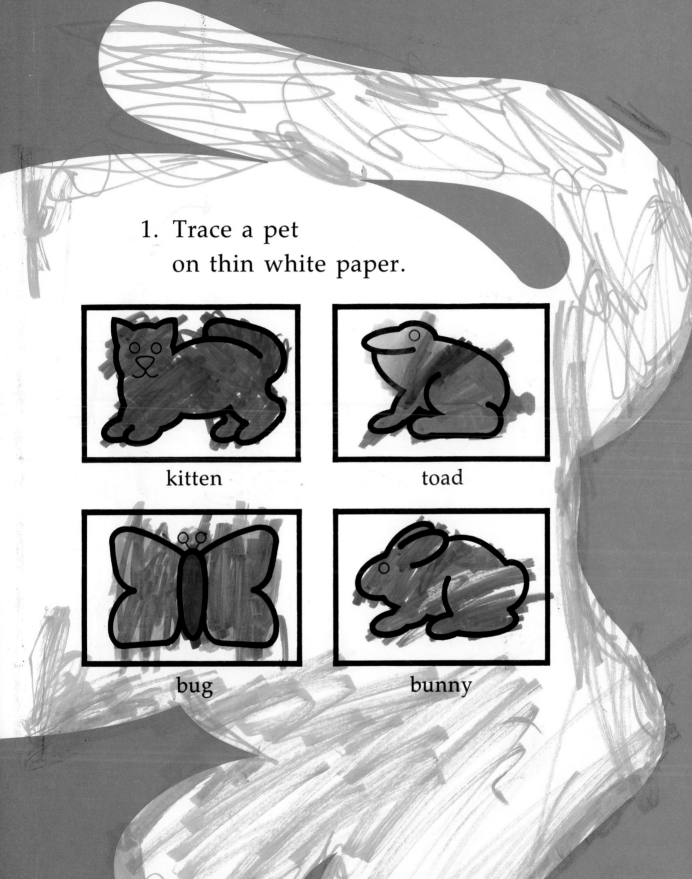

kitten

toad

bug

bunny

2. Color the pet.

3. Cut the pet
   out of the paper
   like this.

4. Cut some paper
   like this.

5. Tape your pet to the paper.

6. Put the paper on your finger and tape the paper like this.

How is that for a pet puppet!

I Was Walking Down the Road

from the book by Sarah E. Barchas

I was walking down the road.
Then I saw a little toad.

I caught it.
I picked it up.
I put it in a cage.

I was jumping on a log.
Then I saw a little frog.

I caught it.
I picked it up.
I put it in a cage.

I was standing on the rug.
Then I saw a little bug.

I caught it.
I picked it up.
I put it in a cage.

I was looking for my mitten.
Then I saw a little kitten.

I caught it.
I picked it up.
I put it in a cage.

I was reading something funny.
Then I saw a little bunny.

I caught it.
I picked it up.
I put it in a cage.

I was looking at my pets.
Then I saw them look at me.

I sat a while.
I thought a while.
And then . . .
I set them free.

43

My Kitten

Kitten, my kitten,
　　Soft and dear,
I am so glad
　　That we are here
Sitting together
　　Just us two
You loving me
　　And me loving you.

—*Marchette Chute*

Go Away, Dog

by Joan Nödset

Go away, you bad dog.
Go away from me.
I don't like you, dog.

I don't like dogs at all.
I don't like big dogs
or little dogs.
I don't like dogs at all.

I don't want that stick.
Don't give it to me.

If I throw the stick,
will you go away?

46

There now, go away
with your stick.

What do you want now?

If I throw the stick
one more time,
will you go away?

Don't jump on me, dog.
I don't like that.

Go away, you old dog.
Go on home now.

Don't you have a home?
Well, that's too bad.
But you can't come home with me.

Don't wag your tail at me.
I don't like dogs.

You are nice for a dog.
But I don't like dogs.

If I play with you,
will you go away?

All right, let's run, dog.
Can you run fast?

You can run fast all right.

49

That was fun, dog.
But I have to go home now.
No, you can't come.
Go away now, dog.

Don't look so sad, dog.
Don't look that way at me.
Can I help it
if you don't have a home?

50

Why don't you go away?

You like me,
don't you, you old dog?
Well, I like you, too.

All right, I give up.

Come on home, dog.
Come on, let's run.

Up and down the street,
 See the people go;
Some move very fast,
 Some move very slow.

Some ride past in cars,
 Some walk on their feet,
The children like to run
 Up
  and   the busy street.
   down

from UP AND DOWN THE STREET
by Lois Lenski

Who's
Next Door ?

The Neighborhood Pet Show

by Stephanie Calmenson

It was the day of the neighborhood pet show.

Kate's pet, Louie, washed while Kate dressed. At breakfast, Kate said to her mom, "I want Louie to win a blue ribbon."

"So do I," said Kate's mom. "But you must not be too sad if he does not win."

Kate looked at Louie and said, "You are a fine pet even if you do not win at the pet show."

"Quack," said Louie. And he did a funny little duck dance.

"We must go now,"
said Kate's mom. "Call Louie."

"Come here, Louie!" said Kate.
"We must go!"

But Louie did not come.
"Quack," he said.
And he ran away.

"Oh, Louie!" said Kate.
"You must come. We must go to
the pet show. I want you to win!"

"Quack, quack," said Louie. He
did not want to go.

"Mom, what will I do?" said Kate.

"There is not a thing you can do,"
said Kate's mom. "If Louie does not
want to come, he will not come."

Kate was sad. She sat and sat.
Then Louie saw how sad Kate was.
He went to her. "Quack!" he said.

"Oh, Mom!" said Kate.
"Louie is here. Now we can
go to the pet show!"

"Welcome to the pet show,"
said Mrs. White. "When I call you,
you may bring your pet up here."

The pets came up one by one.

Kate saw her neighbor Mr. Ling.
He had his cat. Then Kate saw her
friend Sal. Sal walked up with her
rabbit.

"Look," said Kate. "Here comes
our new neighbor with a funny bird."

Then Mrs. White said, "All right, Kate, you may show us your pet now."

Kate went up with Louie. Louie went right up to Mrs. White and said, "Quack, quack!"

"Quack, quack, to you too!" said Mrs. White.

Next Louie did his little duck dance. Everyone thought it was very funny.

Then Louie picked up a ribbon
and showed it to the people.

Mrs. White said, "I think
Louie knows who will win
that ribbon."

And Kate smiled a very
big smile.

New Neighbors

When Smiths packed up
and moved away,
and Judy was gone,
I cried all day.

I knew I'd **never**
like anyone
as much as Judy
or have such fun.

Then Browns moved in
with a silky cat
and a dog with puppies.
Imagine that!

And a girl named Becky . . .
and I forgot
all about missing
Judy a lot.

—Aileen Fisher

63

In the Neighborhood

by Mary C. Lewis

A neighborhood is where people live, work, and play.

Look at this neighborhood. Today you will meet some people in the neighborhood.

Meet Meg. She and her family live in a huge house in this neighborhood. Meg has lots of friends here.

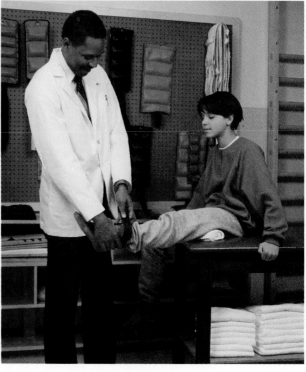

Meet Meg's mom. She is one
of the people who work in this
neighborhood. She works at a pet
shop. Lots of people come to Meg's
mom to ask about pets.

Meet Meg's dad. Meg's dad
works in a hospital. He helps
people get well.

These people work in the
neighborhood too.

Look at the man with the pail.
He is on a ladder washing windows.
The windows will look nice.

Meet Mr. Brown. Mr. Brown brings
mail to the people who live here.

Meet Luke. Luke lives in the neighborhood now. He is Meg's new neighbor.

Meg shows Luke where they can play. They can run and jump here. They can play here every day.

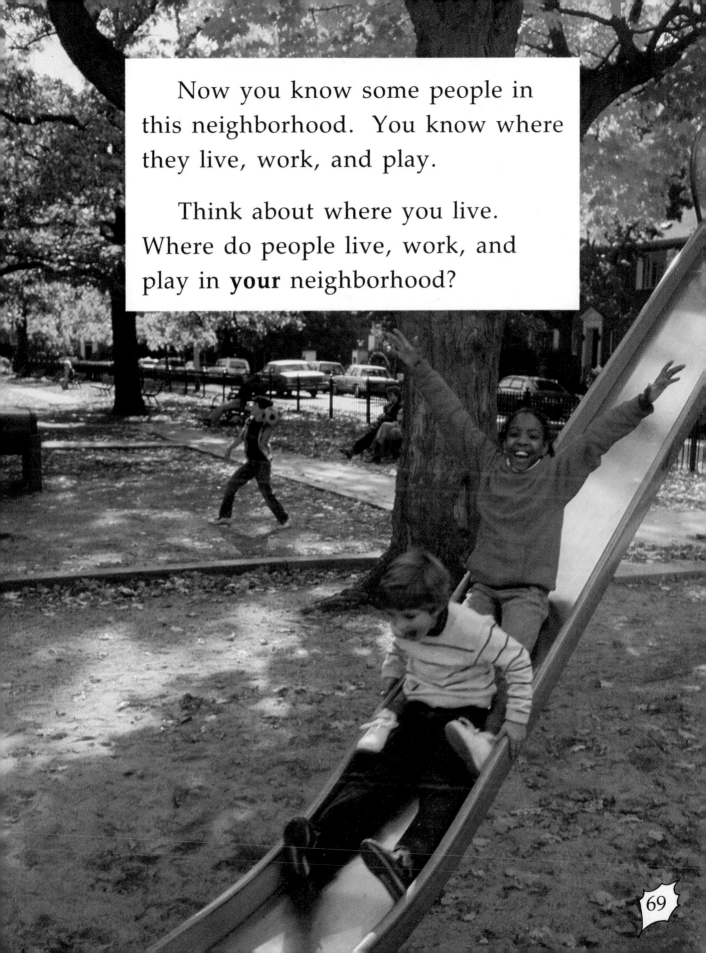

Now you know some people in this neighborhood. You know where they live, work, and play.

Think about where you live. Where do people live, work, and play in **your** neighborhood?

Surprises come
    In such interesting sizes—
I LIKE
    SURPRISES!

from SURPRISES *by Jean Conder Soule*

Surprise! Surprise!

The Climb

by Mitchell Sharmat

"Let's have a race to the top!"
said Kevin.

"I will win," said Drew.

"I want to race, too," said Shari.

"You can't," said Kevin. "You
are too small."

"Stay with me, Shari," said Dad.
"We will have lots of fun."

Kevin and Drew ran to the start of the trail.

"Stop!" said Mom. "Uncle Billy and I must go with you. Kevin will climb with Uncle Billy. Drew can climb with me."

"But we want to race!" said Drew.

"We will race," said Mom.

Dad and Shari said, "Good luck!"

Mom and Drew started walking up the trail. Kevin and Uncle Billy ran past Drew and Mom.

"Hurry! They will win!" said Drew.

"We will see," said Mom.

Drew and Mom climbed and climbed up the trail. They did not see Kevin and Uncle Billy.

"Hurry! Hurry!" said Drew. "Kevin and Uncle Billy must be at the top! They are winning."

"We will see," said Mom.

Then Drew saw Kevin and Uncle Billy. They were not running. They were not walking. They were not climbing. They were having lunch.

"Mom, can we have lunch too?"
Drew asked.

"Let's eat at the top," said Mom.

Mom and Drew climbed past
Kevin and Uncle Billy.

Kevin and Uncle Billy stopped
eating. They started climbing faster
and faster up the trail.

Kevin said, "Hurry! Hurry!
They are winning. They are almost
at the top."

"I'm climbing as fast as I can,"
said Uncle Billy.

"Hurry, Mom!" said Drew.
"Here come Kevin and Uncle Billy.
Hurry, or **they** will win."

"They can't," said Mom. "We are now at the top."

"We won!" said Drew.

"You won," said Kevin.

"No, Dad and I won," said Shari.

"How did **you** get here?" asked Drew.

"We came by bus," said Shari. "See!"

Guess What's Inside

Can you guess what is inside?

Turn the page to see if you are right.

What's inside?

What's inside?

What's inside?

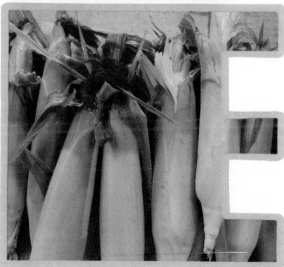

Mr. Fox's Sack

retold by Nora Brooks Blakely

One day Mr. Fox was on his way to his friend's house. He saw a little bird. He grabbed it and put it in his sack.

He walked and walked. Then he came to a little house. A little woman was in the house, cooking.

"Will you watch my sack for me?
I am going to see my friend," said
Mr. Fox.

"All right," said the little woman.

"But you can't look in my sack,"
he said.

"Oh, I will not do that," she said.

So Mr. Fox walked on.

After he was gone, the little
woman looked in the sack. The little
bird got out, and the little woman's
cat ate it.

Well! Mr. Fox was very mad
when he came back. He put the
little woman's cat in his sack and
walked away.

He came to a tall house. A very
tall woman was in the house. She
was washing her hair.

"I am going to see my friend. Will you watch my sack for me?" asked Mr. Fox.

"All right," said the tall woman.

"But you can't look in my sack," he said.

"Oh, I will not do that," she said.

So Mr. Fox walked on.

When he was gone, the tall woman
grabbed the sack and looked in.

"Oh, no!" she said as the cat
jumped out and the tall woman's
son ran after it. The son came back,
but the cat did not.

The fox was very mad when he
came back. He jumped up and down.
Then he put the tall woman's son in
the sack.

Mr. Fox walked and walked and walked. He saw a very big house. A very big woman was in it. She was making brown bread. Three little boys sat with her. A big dog was with her too.

"I am going to see my friend.
Will you watch my sack for me?"
asked Mr. Fox.

"All right," said the big woman.

"But you can't look in my sack,"
he said.

"Oh, I will not do that," she said.

Mr. Fox walked away.

When he was gone, the little boy called out, "Help, help!"

The big woman ran to the sack and looked in.

She said, "Hello! Did Mr. Fox put you in there? If you come out, you may have some bread with us. My sons will have a nice new friend."

"Thank you. I think I will like that," said the little boy.

The big woman helped the boy
out of the sack. She put her big dog
in the sack.

When Mr. Fox came back, he grabbed his sack. He did not say thank you. He just walked away. He walked and walked. Then he sat down.

"I will make this little boy
work for me."

Mr. Fox looked in his sack.
The big dog jumped out. Mr. Fox
ran away.

The big dog went home. And
the very big woman in the very big
house gave him a very big slice of
brown bread.

Whispers
and
Smiles

Whispers
    tickle through your ear
    telling things you like to hear.

from WHISPERS
by Myra Cohn Livingston

Body Talk

by Rose Fiorentino

Hello.
Do you want to play?

Who me?

Yes, you.
Let's play Body Talk.

How do we play that?

103

Whispers

Whispers
    tickle through your ear
    telling things you like to hear.

Whispers
    are as soft as skin
    letting little words curl in.

Whispers
    come so they can blow
    secrets others never know.

—*Myra Cohn Livingston*

The Secret

by Jean Van Leeuwen

Mother and Oliver and Amanda
were sitting in the big chair.

"Tell me a secret," said Oliver.

"All right," said Mother.

Mother whispered a secret
in Oliver's ear: "We are as snug
as three bugs in a rug."

"Tell me too," said Amanda.

"First I have to tell my tiger,"
said Oliver.

Oliver whispered the secret in his tiger's ear: "Three bugs had a hug."

"Now tell me," said Amanda.

Oliver's tiger whispered the secret in Amanda's ear: "Three bugs are on the rug."

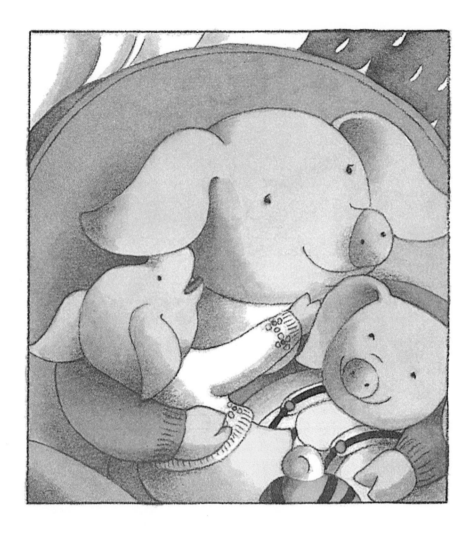

"Can you tell me, Amanda?"
asked Mother.

Amanda whispered the secret
in Mother's ear: "Bug in your ear."

"What bug?" said Mother. "Where?"

Mother jumped up and slapped
the air and slapped her ear.
Oliver and Amanda fell off the chair.
Mother fell on top of them.

"Oh, my," said Mother. She sat up. "Where did the bug go?" she asked.

"There was no bug," said Oliver. "It was just a secret."

Mother laughed. Oliver and Amanda laughed. They laughed and laughed.

"That was a funny secret," said
Mother.

And the three of them had
a very big hug on the rug.

Talk

*an African folktale
retold by Anne L. Ryle*

One day a boy went to pick a flower in his garden. He pulled and pulled on the flower.

"Stop!" said the flower. "Do not pick me. Go away."

"Who said that?" asked the boy.

The dog laughed and said, "It was the flower. It told you to go away."

Then the boy looked at his dog. "Did my dog just talk?" the boy asked.

He went over to the dog. A rock under his foot said, "Get off me!"

"Oh, oh, oh," said the boy, and he ran away.

"Why are you running?" asked the boy's mother. She was making some bread.

"The flower said to go away. The dog said to listen to the flower. And the rock said to get off."

"Is that all?" asked his mother. "Is that so bad?"

"Well," said the bread to the mother, "did he get off the rock?"

"Oh, oh, oh," said the mother. The boy and his mother ran to tell the father. He was making a drum.

"Why are you running to me?" asked the father.

"The flower said to go away.
The dog said to listen to the flower.
The rock said to get off. Then the
bread asked if he did," said the
mother.

"Is that all?" asked the father.
"Is that so bad?"

"Well, did the boy get off the
rock?" asked the drum.

"Oh, oh, oh," said the boy, the mother, and the father. They ran to tell the grandma everything.

The grandma laughed and
laughed. "That is funny. But those
things do not talk. Now go back to
work."

So they went away.

The grandma laughed some more.
Then she sat on her chair.

"Did you ever hear a thing so funny?" asked the chair.

"Who said that?" asked the grandma.

Shhh. Shhh. What do I hear?
Is it something that I fear?
Is it thunder,
Loud and booming?

Are there monsters
Dark and looming?
No, it's not at all like that.
It's just my pouncing, bouncing cat!

SHHH *by Jane Albers*

Who's
Afraid ?

THE THREE LITTLE PIGS

fairy tale retold by Stephanie Calmenson

One day three little pigs set out to make their way in the world.

"Good-bye and take care," said their mother. "Look out for the big bad wolf!"

The three little pigs walked and walked. They saw a man with some straw.

The first little pig said to the man, "Will you give me some straw?"

"Yes, I will," said the man.

So the first little pig made a
house of straw.

Was that a good house?

No, it was not!

The big bad wolf came. He
huffed! And he puffed! And he
blew the house down. The first
little pig ran away.

Two little pigs walked and walked.
They met a man with sticks.

The second little pig said, "Will
you give me some sticks?"

"Yes, I will," said the man.

So the second little pig made a
house of sticks.

Was that a good house?

No, it was not!

The big bad wolf came. He huffed. And he puffed! And he blew the house down! The second little pig ran away.

One little pig walked and walked.
Then he met a man with some bricks.

The third little pig said, "Will
you give me some bricks?"

"Yes, I will," said the man.

So the third little pig made a house of bricks.

Was that a good house?

Oh, yes, it was!

The big bad wolf came. He huffed! And he puffed! But that house did not fall down.

The third little pig saw the first little pig and the second little pig run by his house of bricks. "Come live with me," he said.

Was that a good way to live? Oh, yes, it was!

Something Is There

Something is there
there on the stair
coming down
coming down
stepping with care.
Coming down
coming down
slinkety-sly.

Something is coming and wants to get by.

—Lilian Moore

Steps in the Dark

by Tom Schiele

It was time for bed, but Clara did
not want to go to her room. "I want
to sleep in my tent," she said.

Clara's grandpa stopped reading.
He looked up. "Why do you want
to sleep in the tent?" he asked.

"I want to look at the stars,"
said Clara.

"Aren't you afraid?" asked
Grandpa Harry.

"Afraid of what?" asked Clara.

"When I was your age, I was
afraid of the dark," said Grandpa
Harry.

"Afraid?" said Clara. "I am too old to be afraid."

"That's good to know," said Grandpa Harry.

"Please help me set up the tent," said Clara.

"All right. I will help you take out some blankets too," said Grandpa Harry.

They set up the tent. They put the blankets in the tent. Then Clara said goodnight to her grandpa.

When her grandpa was gone,
Clara made the blankets into a bed.
It was very dark inside the tent.
I am ready to look at the stars now,
thought Clara.

Clara poked her head out of the
tent. It was dark there too. Clara
looked for the stars. She could not see
them. All she could see was the dark.

Just then Clara thought she could hear something. She could not see, but she could hear something come stepping over the grass. What was making those steps in the dark?

Clara was afraid. She looked into the dark. She could not see, but she could hear the steps. They came stepping over the grass, step by step, one at a time.

Clara went into the tent again.
She was afraid. She sat on the
blankets in the dark of her tent. She
could not see, but she could hear the
steps. She got under the blankets.
She could still hear the steps. They
came right up to the tent and
stopped.

Something was standing right
next to the tent. Clara could not see
it, but she could hear it. What was
there?

Suddenly a light went on inside
the tent. Clara looked up.

There was her grandpa.

"What are you doing here?"
asked Clara.

"I didn't want to go to my room,"
said Grandpa Harry. "So I came
to look at the stars with you."

"It is too dark to see the stars,"
said Clara.

"Well, it may be too dark to see
the stars, but it is not too dark to
eat," said Grandpa Harry. "See, I
have a bag of popcorn."

"That I **can** see!" said Clara.

Picture This!

I'm painting a picture,
    A beautiful one,
But no one can see it
    Until it is done.

It isn't an engine.
    It isn't a rose.
And when I will finish it
    Nobody knows.

ART *by Marchette Chute*

A Man

I like to draw a man,
He stands up big and tall,
He has a head on top,
It's round just like a ball.
Below he has a neck
And shoulders very wide,
I'll give him nice long arms
To stretch out at each side.
His coat has buttons big,
And on his arms are hands,
His legs are very long,
And on his feet he stands.
I like to draw a man
So big and strong and tall,
And when my drawing's done
I'll hang it on the wall.

—Lois Lenski

Drawing Animals

from ED EMBERLEY'S DRAWING BOOK OF ANIMALS
by Ed Emberley

You can have fun drawing animals. Just read the steps below. Then look at the boxes on the next page.

1. Look at the top of the page. Read the name of the animal.

2. Look at the first box. Draw what you see.

3. Look at the second box. Add the new thing that you see.

4. Do the same for all the boxes. When you get to the last box, you will have a drawing of an animal.

PIG

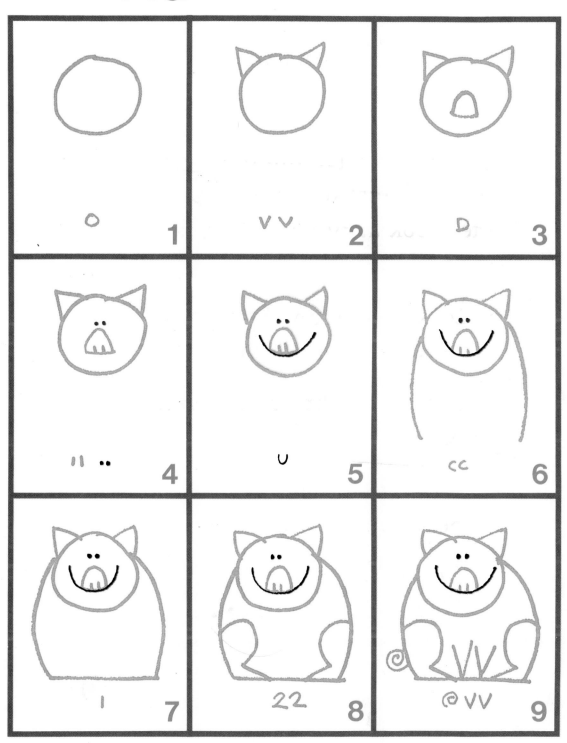

FROG

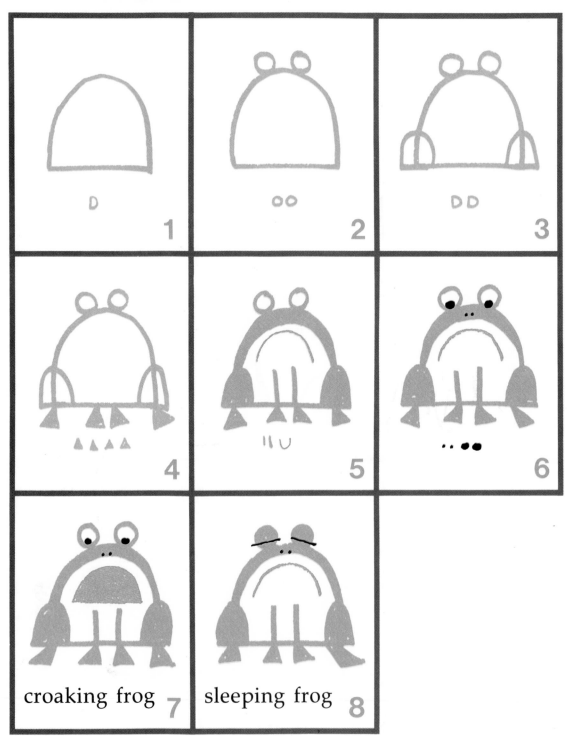

croaking frog 7

sleeping frog 8

OWL

Willaby

by Rachel Isadora

Willaby is in first grade.
She likes math. She likes
lunch. And she likes
her teacher Miss Finney.
But best of all Willaby
likes to draw.

When the other children
play, Willaby draws.

Willaby draws at home too.

One morning when Willaby went to school, Miss Finney was not there. Mrs. Benjamin said that Miss Finney was sick and could not come to school all week.

The children wanted to give Miss Finney get-well cards. They made up a poem. Mrs. Benjamin put it on the blackboard.

Soon everyone was putting the
poem on cards. But not Willaby.
She was drawing a fire truck.

After a little while, Mrs. Benjamin asked the children to hand in their cards. Willaby did not know what to do. She had not made a get-well card. There was no time to put the poem on a card. Willaby passed in her drawing.

All the other children passed in their cards.

On the way home from school,
Willaby thought of her drawing.
She had not put her name on it!

How was Miss Finney going to
know that Willaby had made the
drawing!

What if Miss Finney thought
Willaby did not like her?

All week at home Willaby made lots and lots of get-well cards for Miss Finney. She put her name on every one of them.

But when Monday morning came,
Willaby did not feel like going to
school.

Dear Willaby,
Thank you for the get-well picture.

Miss Finney

Willaby walked to school with her head down. Willaby was sad. She walked to her seat. She did not look at Miss Finney. But when she sat down at her seat . . .

Willaby did not give Miss Finney
all the get-well cards. She did not
have to!

Growing Up

When I was One,
I had just begun.

When I was Two,
I was nearly new.

When I was Three,
I was hardly Me.

When I was Four,
I was not much more.

When I was Five,
I was just alive.

But now I am Six, I'm clever as clever.
So I think I'll be six now for ever and ever.

THE END *by A. A. Milne*

JOHN
4½

KATE
3½
John
age 3

John
Age 2½

KATE
AGE 2

Animal Babies Grow Up

by *Mary C. Lewis*

Animals must take care
of their babies.

A mother bear takes good care of her baby bears. She keeps them warm in the winter when they are little babies.

She helps them catch fish to eat. She keeps them safe.

When the next winter comes, the bears are big. Then they can go off alone.

Mother and father foxes take care
of their babies. At first, baby foxes
can't see so they need help. The
mother fox must bring them food
to eat.

The mother and father look out
for the baby foxes. When the babies
can see, the mother or father shows
them how to catch mice and rabbits.
Baby foxes stay with their family
while they grow up.

Mother and father owls take care
of their babies too.

They help the baby owls eat. The
mother and father have to get a lot
of food for them to eat.

Mother and father owls are like teachers. They show the baby owls how to catch bugs to eat. They show the baby owls how to fly.

With help, the baby owls will grow up to know many things.

Bears, foxes, and owls take care
of their babies in many ways. Many
other animals do too.

Owly

by Mike Thaler

Owly started asking questions
when he was two years old. He
would sit all night with his mother
under the stars.

"How many stars are in the sky?"
he asked one night.

"Many," answered his mother.

"How many?" asked Owly,
looking up.

His mother smiled. "Count them."

"One, two, three, four . . ."

"One hundred and one, one hundred and two, one hundred and three, one hundred and four . . ."

Owly was still counting when the sun came up. "One thousand and one, one thousand and two . . ."

179

"How many stars are in the sky?" asked his mother.

"More than I can count," said Owly, blinking.

And he tucked his head under his wing, and went to sleep.

The next night Owly looked up at the sky again.

"How high is the sky?" he asked his mother.

181

"Very high," she said, looking up.

"How high?" asked Owly.

"Go and see," said his mother.

So Owly flew up into the sky. He flew high above his tree. He flew to the clouds. He flapped his wings very hard. He flew above the clouds. But as high as he could fly, the sky was always higher.

In the morning when he landed
on the tree, he was very tired.

"How high is the sky?" asked his
mother.

"Higher than I can fly," said
Owly, closing his eyes and falling
asleep.

The next night Owly heard the sound of the waves in the ocean.

"How many waves are there in the ocean?" he asked his mother.

"Many waves," she answered.

"How many?" asked Owly.

"Go and count them," she replied.

So Owly flew to the shore.
He stood on the beach and counted
the waves.

"One, two, three, four . . ."

But as many as he could count,
many more followed.

"One thousand and one,
one thousand and two . . ."

And when the sun came up, he
saw that there was still an ocean full
of waves.

So, sleepily, he returned to his
mother.

"How many waves are in the
ocean?" she asked.

"More than I can count,"
answered Owly, closing his eyes.

The next night Owly asked his mother, "How **deep** is the ocean?"

"Very deep," she answered.

"How deep?" asked Owly.

His mother looked at the sky.
"Almost as deep as the sky is high,"
she said.

Owly looked up. He sat there all night thinking about the sky, and the stars, and the waves, and the ocean, and all he had learned from his mother.

And as the sun came up he turned to her and said, "I love you."

"How much?" asked his mother.

"Very much," answered Owly.

"How much?" she asked.

Owly thought for a minute and then gave her a hug. "I love you as much as the sky is high and the ocean is deep."

She put her wing around him and gave him a hug.

"Do you have any more hugs to give me?" asked Owly.

"Many more." His mother
hugged him again.

"How many more?" asked Owly,
falling asleep.

"As many as there are waves in
the ocean and stars in the sky."

And she did.